NO MORE MiLK

Written by Rhiannon Henderson

Illustrated by Vikkireds

ISBN: 978-0-9923972-2-7

"To my darling little girl,
you have the sweetest soul, and I'm honoured to be
your mother. Thank you for the inspiration to be
the best version of myself that I can be."
🖤

Hello!

If you've picked up my little story book, chances are you're hoping for some tools to help you with night weaning your little one from breastfeeding, and they're at the age where you are hoping that books, repetition, and gentle parenting will help with the transition.

Night weaning, or total weaning can be such an overwhelming thought. Whatever the reason you find yourself with this book in your hands, you should know that it's okay to night wean whenever you're ready.

When I first started feeding my daughter, we struggled with things like tongue ties, and bottle preference, milk supply.. the list goes on. I definitely fought hard for our feeding relationship, and I had hoped we'd continue it until she self weaned. My goal was always two years, as is the World Heath Organisation's recommendation, and as we approached that two year mark, I definitely felt it was time to start to wean.

I felt shame, that I wanted to end something my daughter was so attached to, but my body hadn't been my own for so long and I needed it back. I even felt guilty that I'd tried so hard to get here and was now choosing to end it.. i know, two years was an epic effort, but weaning can be full of many emotions we can't quite explain.

We night weaned first, replacing milk with cuddles and teddies throughout the the night. We read a few books, and I would read her this one too, sitting in a file on my phone, showing her photos of the fun things we would do if we slept through the night!

Eventually about a month after night weaning, I started distracting her with other things when she asked for milk during the day. After about a week, we were only feeding before bed at night, and then at twenty six months exactly we had our last feed.

I found that gentle weaning worked for us, and reading books really helped her understand that there was no more milk. Overnight if she'd wake, I'd often say, "remember we said no more milk at night, it's dark outside! Tomorrow I want to go to the park so I need to get some sleep. Would you like a cuddle?". To be honest she mostly said no and threw herself on the bed with a big sigh and went back to sleep.

We did attempt to night wean a couple of times, and it just wasn't the right time for us. If you don't feel ready or comfortable, try again in a couple of weeks. You will know when it's the right time for your family.

Your body has done an incredible thing, to nourish your child for so long. You are an amazing parent for dedicating yourself to your feeding journey, and it's okay to choose the time to wean on your own terms.

I hope this story, from our family to yours, helps you and your little one on your own weaning journey, whenever the time is right for you.

Love,
Rhiannon
(and Beatrix!)

It's time to go to sleep my love,
It's time to close our eyes

The two of us will snuggle close
And soon the sun will rise.

I know when you were very small,
you needed milk to sleep,

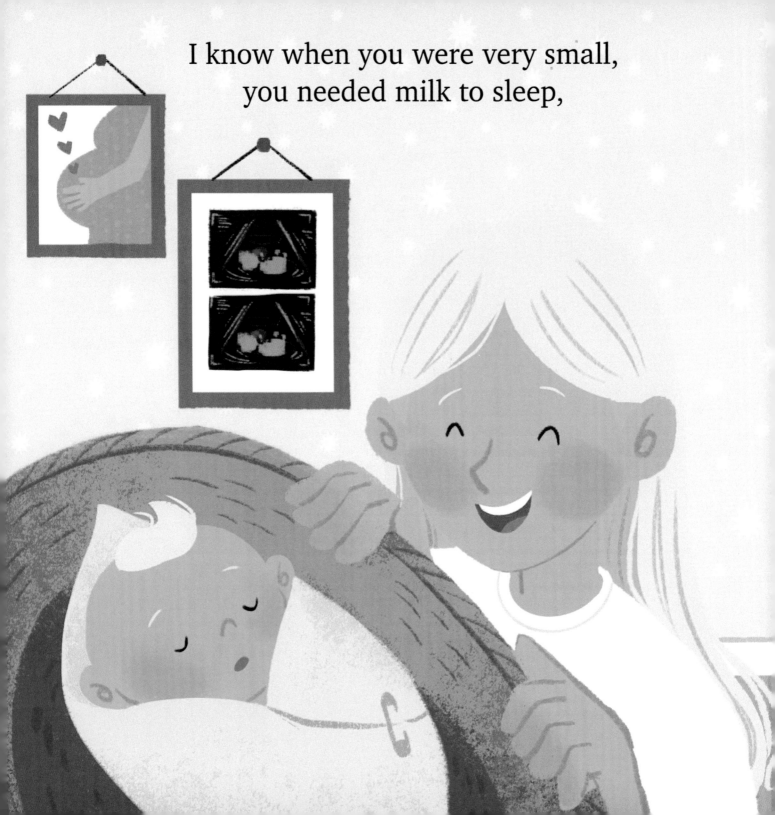

But now that you are getting tall
A cuddle is all you need.

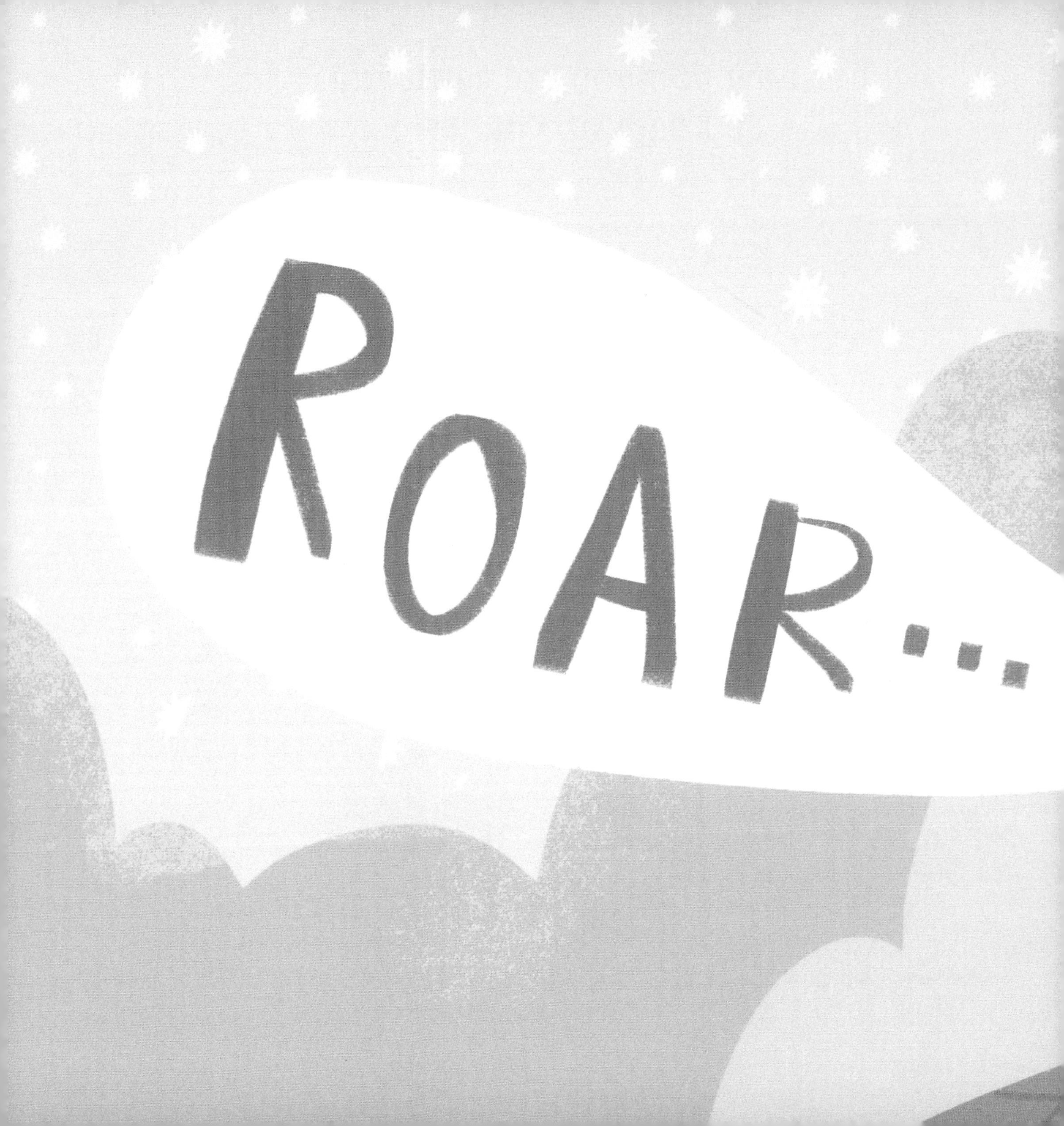
ROAR...

It's okay, just let it out
I know it makes you sad
I still love you just the same
Even when you're feeling mad

Without my milk all through the night,
We'll have a better sleep,
And when the sun is shining bright,
We can do your favourite things.

We can listen to a song

Or go out for a walk

We can make some silly faces,
Or talk some silly talk.

We can paint, or draw a picture

We can sing and
dance as well,

We can read some silly books,
Or practice show and tell.

We can play at the playground,
Or blow bubbles at the park,

We can do all that because we'll sleep,
With no more milk in the dark

So it's time to go to sleep my love,
It's time to close our eyes
The two of us will snuggle close
And soon the sun will rise.

The End

Made in the USA
Coppell, TX
14 December 2024

42577552R00019